I will DANCE ACROSS the MORNING SKY

MARCIA McGEE ASHFORD

Illustrated By: Sudipta (Steve) Dasgupta

Copyright

ISBN 978-1-7362294-4-6 Hardback Edition
ISBN 978-1-7362294-3-9 Paperback Edition
ISBN 978-1-7362294-5-3 e-Book edition

Disclaimer: This book is written as a celebration of life through words and art. It is not intended as a substitute for medical advice, counseling, or anything that might require diagnosis or medical attention.

Marcia Ashford-Heartstring Productions, LLC
Huntsville, Alabama

Printed in the United States of America First Printing, 2020
Library of Congress Control Number: 2020924597

Personal Dedication

To Carl Everette and Opal McGee for being incredible parents and always believing in me.

To Randy Ashford for your unconditional love and our two children.

To Amber and Alex, my heart and joy, thank you for being my daughter and son. I love you beyond words.

To family and friends, here and on the other side of life, for lifting me up with your wings during tough times.

Dedication to Readers

This book is dedicated to those who have loved and lost. May you find some comfort here.

Acknowledgments

I would like to acknowledge Sudipta "Steve" Dasgupta for all his hard work on the illustrations of this book. He spent several months working with me, discussing the feeling of the lines when necessary, and doing countless revisions to bring each page to life. Thank You Sudipta for creating a masterpiece that will be a precious heirloom for everyone.

I will dance,
across the morning sky

Soar above golden clouds

Twirl and swirl into
the colors of a rainbow

Swim with dolphins

Turn invisible summersaults
in the salty sand

Drift into the evening stars
and beyond

I'll sing in the heavenly choir

Try on halos,
til I find one that's a perfect fit

Visit those who left before me

Think of me
and I will think of you.

That penny you find? The redbird?
Feathers?
All signs my love for you never dies

Days, months, years pass
as I continue my adventures

and you live your life

Someday, Somehow
We will meet again

And Hug, laugh
Visit loved ones

Chase falling stars

Make cloud angels

And together sit
at the feet of God

I will Dance Across the Morning Sky

I will dance across the morning sky

Soar above golden clouds

Twirl and swirl into the colors of a rainbow

Swim with dolphins

Turn invisible summersaults in the salty sand

Drift into the evening stars and beyond

I'll sing in the heavenly choir

Try on halos til I find one that's a perfect fit

Explore the universe

Visit those who left before me

Think of me and I will think of you

That penny you find? The redbird? Feathers?

All signs my love for you never dies

Days, months, years pass

as I continue my adventures and you live your life

Someday

Somewhere

We will meet again

And

Hug, laugh

Visit loved ones

Chase falling stars

Make cloud angels

And together sit at the feet of God

———— ◆ ————

About the Author

Author Marcia McGee Ashford is founder of Heartstring Productions LLC, which supports writers, musicians, and artists with a heart for the arts. She is also a college professor and has her doctorate in Christian Counseling. Her main goal in life is to make a difference.

When she lost her husband one of the places she turned to for comfort was books and journaling. Out of that grief and loss came the poem I Will Dance Across the Sky. It is written as a celebration of life, to commemorate and rejoice in a life well lived. It offers love and compassion for those who are left behind when a loved one passes.

She writes cancer support books and shares her personal experiences, faith, hope, and humor to encourage those on the journey.

Her children's books are full of light and joy. She creates unique characters, talking animals, imaginary worlds, and turns them into a delightful read for kids.

Marcia is proud mom to Amber and Alex and her fur baby Lexi Grace. More information can be found on her website: www.heartstringproductions.com

About the Illustrator

Sudipta Dasgupta, also known as Steve, began drawing with chalk on the floor when he was around 3 years old. Later, he joined a local art school near Kolkata City, India. After his school final, he enrolled in the science stream to pursue higher education. He soon realized he wanted something different than the stereotypical schooling system, and took on the challenge of getting accepted into a good art college. In the year 2006, he graduated from the Government College of Art and Craft at the University of Calcutta.

Initially, Sudipta spent many years practicing painting on canvas with different mediums. Then in 2009, he began to get offers to work on storybook illustrations from many companies and individual authors. Since then, he has been a full-time book illustrator and has worked with more than a hundred and seventy-five companies and individual authors worldwide. Aside from book illustration, he also enjoys craft, painting, graphic design, murals, as well as many other forms of art. For more information about Sudipta Steve Dasgupta, please visit : www.dasguptarts.com

Made in the USA
Las Vegas, NV
10 August 2021